LOONEY TUNES™

Pedigree® BOOKS

Published by Pedigree Books Limited
The Old Rectory, Matford Lane, Exeter, EX2 4PS

£6.99

LT3

FUN FUN FUN FUN

that's the theme of the Mil Looney Um.

Forget the grown-up's boring Millennium; we have the ideal family alternative. Look out for chances to win amazing prizes, collect fantastic gizmos and take part in the party of the year. The Looney Tunes are everywhere and want to recruit you to spread the message. The Mil-Looney-Um is fun, are you fun enough to handle it?

You can also…

PARTY ROUND YOUR VIDEO

Warner Home Video will be releasing a special Mil-Looney-Um Looney Tunes Bumper compilation, so you can watch the greatest toons whenever you want and as many times as you want! It will be available from the October 1999 half term from all major retail outlets.

PARTY ROUND THE STORES

Every day will be party day at the Warner Bros. Studio Stores. There'll be plenty of entertainment including parties, karaoke, congas and line-dancing. Your favourite characters will be making star appearances

and there'll be lots of exclusive Mil-Looney-Um souvenirs to buy.

PARTY ROUND THE CINEMA

Warner Village Cinemas will be organising Taz-tic special screenings, Kids Club Events, giveaways and Fun in the Foyer events at all their UK multiplexes, to build up to an amazing holiday competition where you can choose which Warner Village Cinema you want to go to - anywhere in the world!

Writer: Michael Eury   Penciller: Pablo Zamboni   Inker: Ruben Torreiro   Letterer: John Costanza   Colors: Prismacolor

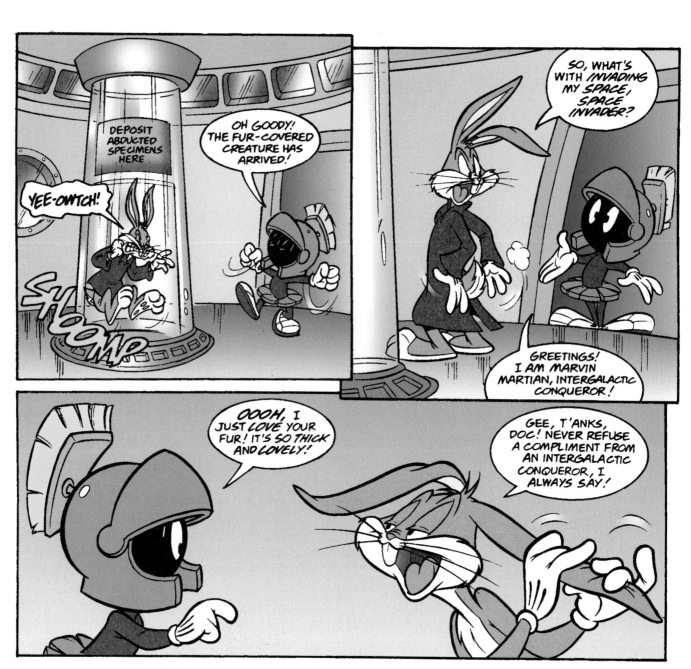

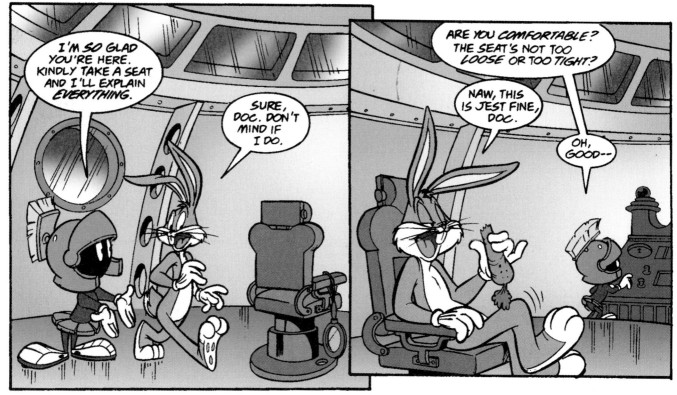

9

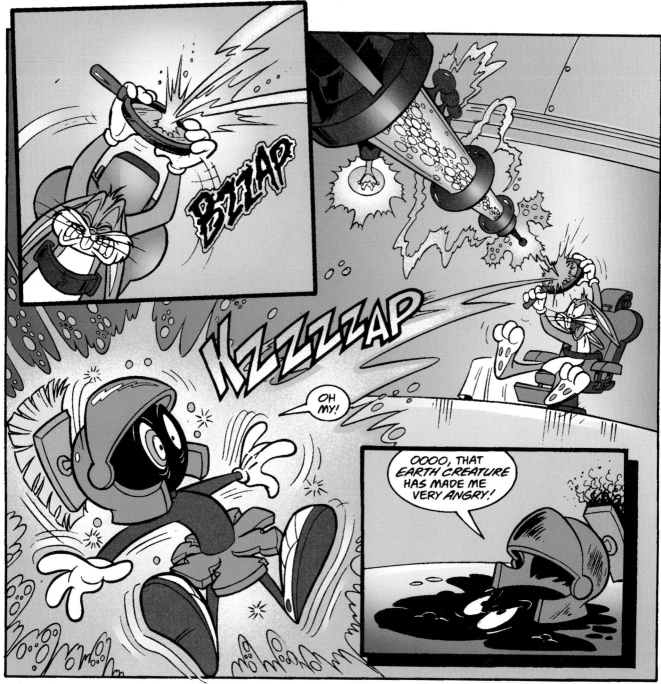

13

14

16

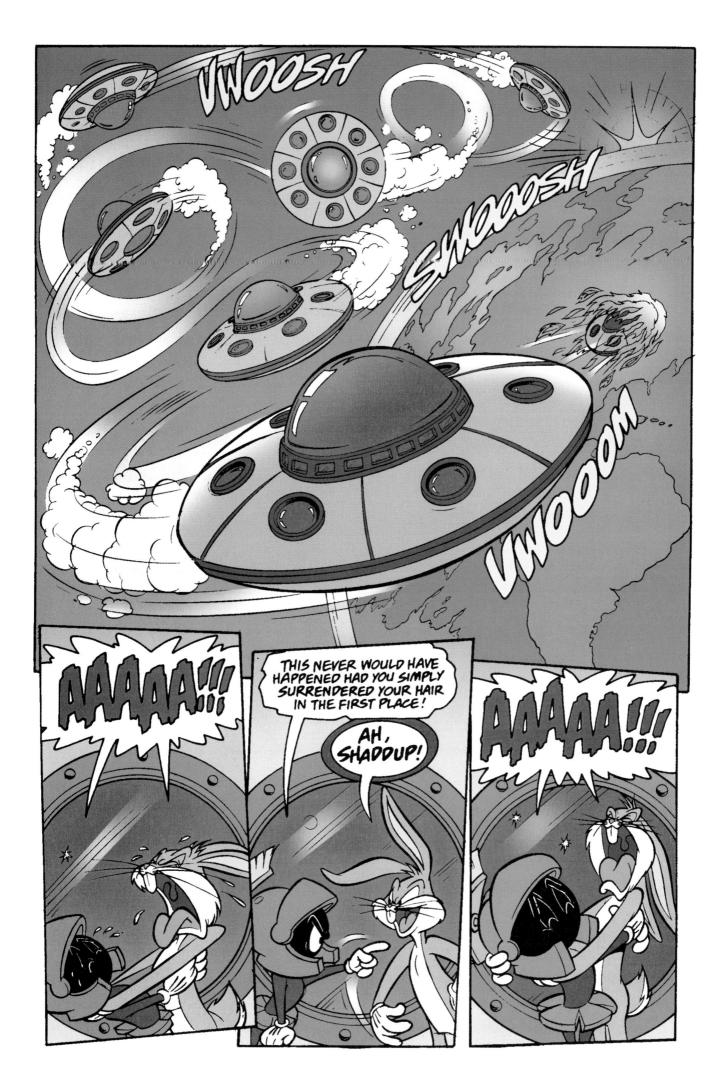

18

SYLVESTER'S COOL CAT COLLECTION

Poor old Sylvester! He's spent all day whizzing around with his rocket pack, trying to catch Tweety Pie. Now his fuel has run out and he's forced to float helplessly in space, waiting for help to arrive!

To pass the time, Sylvester has thought of 15 words beginning with the letters CAT. Find out what they are by solving the clues and writing your answers in the boxes, using the letters already in place to guide you.

1. A naughty boy's weapon made from a Y-shaped twig

| C | A | T | I | P | O | L | T |

2. Lots of bulls and cows

| C | A | T | T | L | E |

3. A wriggly insect which turns into a butterfly

| C | A | T | e | p | i | l | l | a | r |

4. A special sailing boat with two hulls

| C | A | T | a | M | a | r | a | n |

5. A big church, usually with two spires

| C | A | T | h | e | d | R | a | l |

6. Goalkeepers, wicket keepers and rugby players do this with a ball

| C | A | T | c | h |

7. A pretty, spinning firework which you nail to a fence (2 words)

| C | A | T | h | e | r | i | n | e | - | W | h | e | e | L |

8. Yellow flower of willow or hazel tree, seen in spring

| C | A | T | k | I | n |

9. A big, fat book full of things you can buy

| C | A | T | a | l | o | G | u | e |

10. A famous T.V quiz show, hosted buy Roy Walker

| C | A | T | c | h | P | h | r | a | s | e |

11. An angry shout or boo at a theatre or concert

| C | A | T | c | a | l | L |

12. A terrible accident or disaster

| C | A | T | a | s | t | r | a | P | h | e |

13. A group or subject that belongs together, usually in a book or at the library

| C | A | T | e | g | o | r | Y |

14. Little reflectors along the middle of the road (2 words)

| C | A | T | s | e | Y | e | s |

15. A girls' game, played buy winding wool or string round your hands (2 words)

| C | A | T | s | c | R | a | d | l | e |

TEN PIN TWEETY

There are 10 SMALL DIFFERENCES between these two pictures of Tweety Pie enjoying himself at the Space Superbowl. Can you spot them all?

Then, using the picture to guide you, colour in the bottom picture with your crayons or felt-tips.

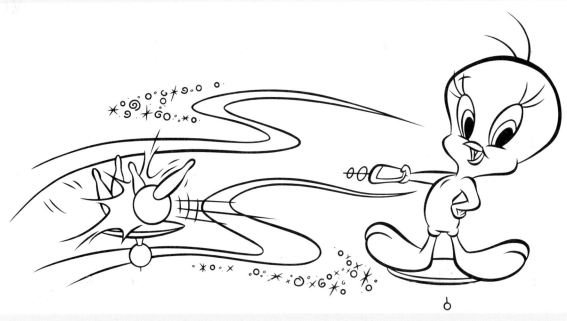

Writers: S. Carolan & J. Moore Pencils: David Alvarez Inks: Mike DeCarlo Letters: John Costanza Colors: David Tanguay

21

26

ANYONE FOR SPACE TENNIS?

Daffy Duck is bursting with energy as usual and has taken all his sports equipment up into Space in the hope of finding some action!
Unscramble the letters of these sporty activities to find the names of Daffy's favourite Earth sports.

Then transfer the **last** letter of each one to the box at the bottom and spell out what Daffy likes to do after a hectic day's exercise.

1. D R S U E O N R — — — — — — — —

2. T B L L O O A F — — — — — — — —

3. N C E A D — — — — —

4. Y C L E C — — — — —

5. M P H I U J G H — — — — — — — —

After exercising all day, Daffy likes to .... — — — — —

Answers: 1. ROUNDERS 2. FOOTBALL 3. DANCE 4. CYCLE 5. HIGHJUMP SLEEP!

A PIZZA MY MIND

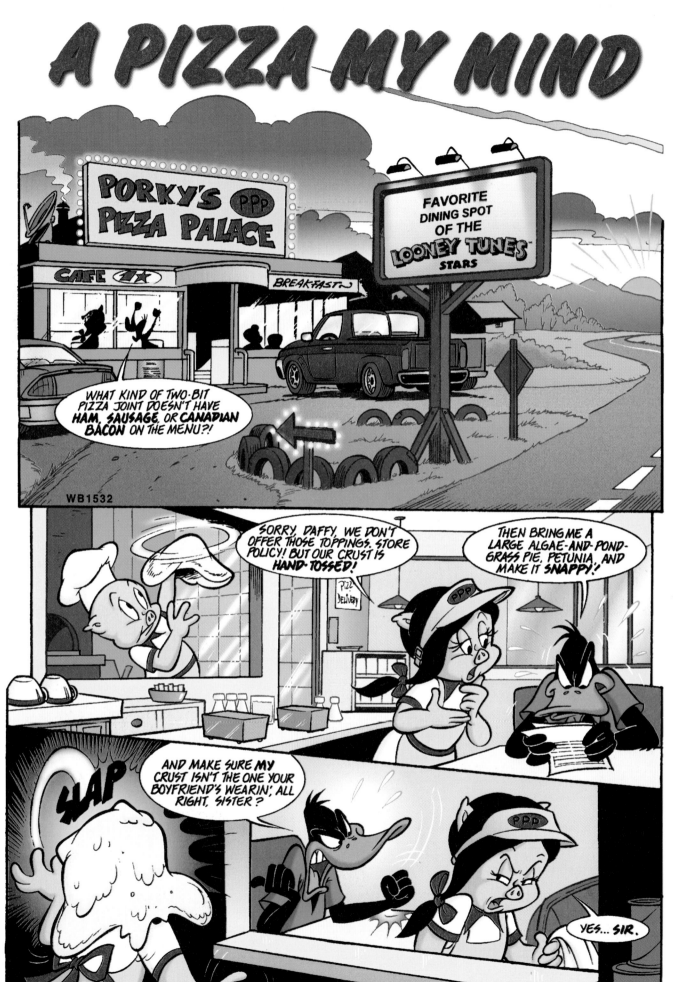

Writer: Michael Eury   Penciller: Horacio Saavedra   Inker: Ruben Torreiro   Letterer: Javier Saavedra   Colorist: David Tanguay

LOONEY TUNES Photo Gallery.

WAAAIT A MINUTE... SOMEONE'S MISSING!

A-A-ACTUALLY, DAFFY, THERE'S--

THERE'S SOMETHIN' ROTTEN HERE, AND IT AIN'T YOUR LIMBURGER AND GARLIC PIZZA!

HEY, PORKSTER-- YOU'VE EVEN GOT THE LOONEY TUNES PROPS UP HERE! SO HOW COME THERE'S NO PICTURE OF ME ON THE WALL ??!

BUGS BUNNY

IT'S THE SMELL OF DUCK DISCRIMINATION!

OF COURSE NOT, DAFFY, THE REASON YOUR P-P-PICTURE ISN'T HERE IS--

--IS THAT YOU DON'T HAVE AN APPROPRIATE SHOT THAT TRULY CAPTURES MY UNPAR- ALLELED HANDSOMENESS! RIGHT?!

THEN SAY NO MORE, PORKY-- I'LL SEE THAT YOU GET ONE.

29

30

31

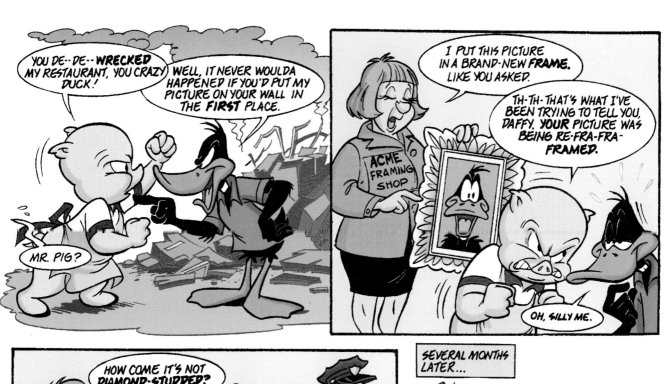

LOLA'S SPACE RIDDLE

Lola's looking as lovely as ever in her special designer spacesuit. But she has left one vital item of beauty equipment back on Earth.

Find out what it is by solving this riddle. Each line leads you to a letter which you write in the box at the bottom.

MY FIRST IS IN LARGE AND ALSO IN LITTLE,

MY SECOND'S IN PINK, IN WINK AND IN SKITTLE.

MY THIRD IS IN PRINCE, BUT NEVER IN LUCK,

MY FOURTH IS IN SOAP, IN SAIL AND IN STUCK.

MY FIFTH IS IN TIME AND ALSO IN STINK,

MY SIXTH IS IN BRICK, IN LICK AND IN INK.

MY SEVENTH'S IN CROWN, IN COW AND IN CRAG,

MY EIGHTH IS IN KICK, BUT NEVER IN FLAG...

SO WHAT ITEM'S MISSING FROM LOLA'S MAKE-UP BAG?

_ _ _ _ _ _ _ _

TERRY COLLINS WRITER • NELSON LUTY PENCILLER • HORACIO OTTOLINI INKS • COMICRAFT LETTERS • PRISMACOLOR COLORS

WB1531

40

WHO WILL WIN THE SPACE RACE?

Look at Bugs and Daffy racing each other in their high-speed space cars! One minute Daffy's in the lead.... then Bugs overtakes...then Daffy's first again.But who is going to win?
In fact, neither of them can win because, just round the corner of the nearest planet, lurks a major problem! Find out what it is by solving this pairs puzzle. Think what goes with the word on the left and write your answer in the box on the right. The first letters, reading downwards, will spell what stopped the race!

QUESTION and

SPICK and

TIME and

BACON and

ROCK 'n'

ON and

PEN and

UP and

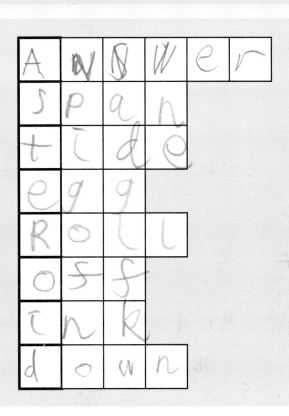

A	N	S	W	e	r
S	p	a	n		
t	i	d	e		
e	g	g			
R	o	l	l		
o	f	f			
i	n	k			
d	o	w	n		

Porky's SPACE STORY

Porky Pig has found the perfect way to relax! He has put his spaceship onto automatic pilot and is speeding round the Solar System, listening to a story cassette. But what story is coming through the headphones?

Find out by solving this puzzle. Read the clues and write your answers into the grid. Then each letter in the grid will have a reference (A3, C5 and so on.) Using these references, work out the coded story title.

	A	B	C	D	E
1	S	t	o	o	l
2	h	u	r	r	y
3	v	o	i	c	e
4	f	r	o	g	s
5	p	o	n	d	s

1 — YOU SIT AT THIS TO HAVE YOUR DINNER

2 — MAKE HASTE

3 — YOU SPEAK AND SING WITH THIS

4 — SMALL GREEN ANIMALS THAT JUMP AND CROAK

5 — POOLS OF WATER WHERE THE ABOVE ANIMALS LIVE

A1,A2,E1   B1,D5,A3,E1,C5,A1,B2,C2,E1,E4
_S_ _h_ _e_   _I_ _d_ _v_ _e_ _n_ _t_ _S_ _ _ _ _

B3,A4,   A1,A2,E1
_o_ _f_   _S_ _ _ _

A1,A2,C2,E1,E1
_S_ _ _ _ _

D1,C3,A1,A1,D1,E1   A5,C3,D4,E4
_ _ _ _ _ _   _ _ _ _

WB1458

45

46

NO, NOTHING SO *DRASTIC!* MY FRIEND, *YOU*, ARE A *FRUSTRATED* FELLOW! YOU HUNT RABBITS..."*HARES*"... IN A SUBCONSCIOUS QUEST TO RECLAIM YOUR OWN LOST "*HAIR*"!

I AM? I DO?

I'VE CHECKED YOUR MEDICAL CHARTS. THERE'S NO *SCIENTIFIC* REASON WHY YOU ARE BALD! IT'S ALL IN YOUR *HEAD*...SO TO SPEAK

I PREDICT IF YOU CAN START BEING *NICE* TO RABBITS, YOUR HAIR WILL COME BACK AND END THIS *DESTRUCTIVE* CYCLE.

STOP CHASING WABBITS? I DUNNO... I GUESS I COULD *TWY*...

OKAY! I'LL STAWT FIWST THING *TOMOWWOW!* THANKS FOR EVEWYTHING, *DOCTOR NOGGIN!*

SAY, WHERE'S MY *GUN?*

OH, I'LL HOLD ONTO THAT UNTIL YOU'VE *COMPLETED* THE TREATMENT...

...AND AFTER YOU'VE GOTTEN MY *BILL!*

48

49

TWO WEEKS LATER...

BOY, SURE HAS BEEN *QUIET* SINCE FUDDSIE GAVE UP CHASIN' ME AROUND THE FOREST.

USUALLY, I AIN'T ONE TO *MEDDLE*, BUT I THINK HE NEEDS A LITTLE *NUDGE* BACK INTA ACTION, COITESY OF AL'S BAKERY.

DING! DONG!

YES...? WHO IS IT?

SPLAT!

OH, HEWWO, WABBIT. *PWEASE*, COME *INSIDE*-- WOULD YOU WIKE A COLD GWASS OF *MILK?* I JUST WOVE MILK WITH PIE! OR WOULD YOU PWEFER *CAWWOT JUICE?*

CARROT JUICE? NOW YOU'RE TALKING, DOC! I'LL TAKE A SIP OR TWO, --SURE

NOW CUT DAT OUT! YOU AIN'T SUPPOSED TO BE *POLITE* AFTER I BEAN YOU WITH A PIE!

I'M NOT?

NO! YOU'RE SCARIN' ME WID THE "KINDER, GENTLER" ACT!

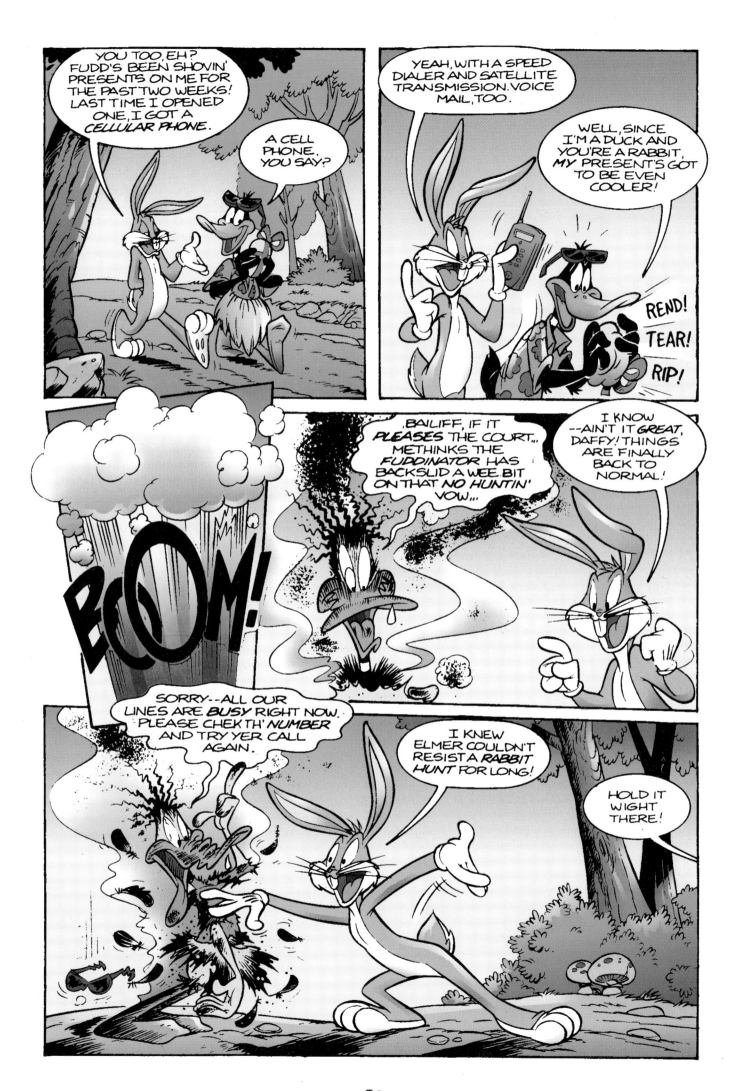

53

54

TAZ'S TEA TIME TEASER

Taz is hungry. (What's new?). As he zooms wildly through space on his supersonic scooter, his eagle eye spots a yummy picnic that has floated up from a passing planet.
But, at the last minute, a shower of meteorites gets between Taz and his tea. There is only ONE path between the flying stones. Can you help Taz by finding it?

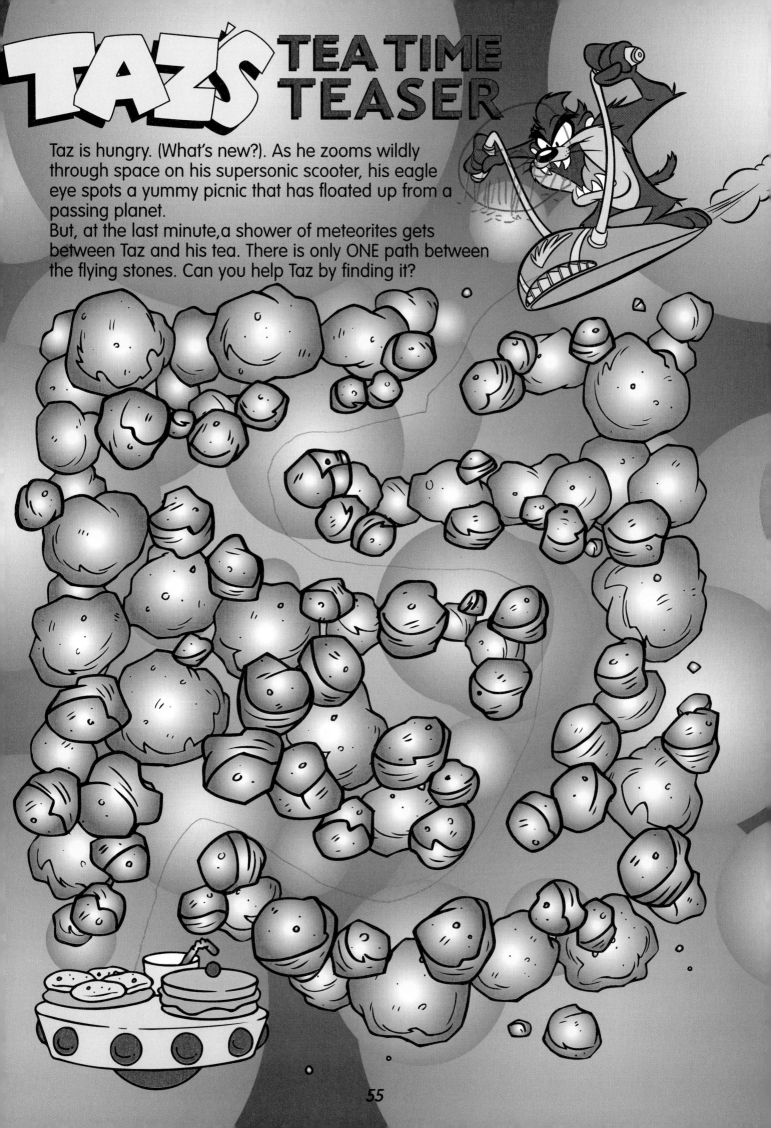

55

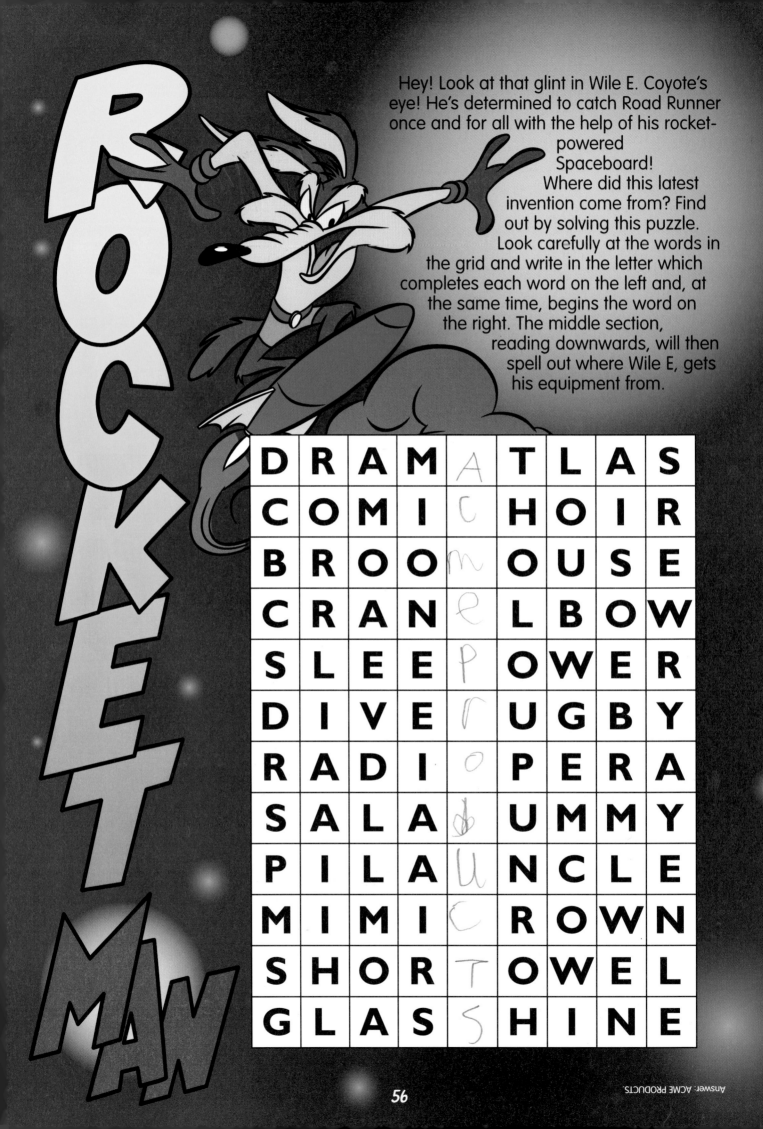

ROCKET MAN

Hey! Look at that glint in Wile E. Coyote's eye! He's determined to catch Road Runner once and for all with the help of his rocket-powered Spaceboard! Where did this latest invention come from? Find out by solving this puzzle. Look carefully at the words in the grid and write in the letter which completes each word on the left and, at the same time, begins the word on the right. The middle section, reading downwards, will then spell out where Wile E, gets his equipment from.

D	R	A	M	A	T	L	A	S
C	O	M	I	C	H	O	I	R
B	R	O	O	M	O	U	S	E
C	R	A	N	E	L	B	O	W
S	L	E	E	P	O	W	E	R
D	I	V	E	R	U	G	B	Y
R	A	D	I	O	P	E	R	A
S	A	L	A	D	U	M	M	Y
P	I	L	A	U	N	C	L	E
M	I	M	I	C	R	O	W	N
S	H	O	R	T	O	W	E	L
G	L	A	S	S	H	I	N	E

56

Writer: Michael Eury   Penciller: Oscar Saavedra   Inker: Ruben Torreiro   Letterer: Javier Saavedra   Colorist: Dave Tanguay

70

ROAD RUNNER DOUBLE TAKE

Knowing Wile E. Coyote is looking for him in Space, clever old Road Runner has returned to Earth for a few hours peace! Look carefully at these six pictures of Road Runner. Only two of them are exactly the same. Can you spot the matching pair?

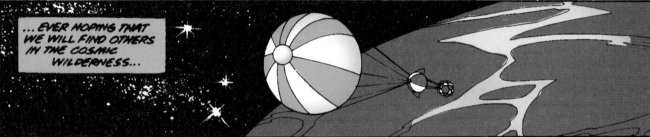

Writer: Dave King Penciller: Nelson Luty (Sol Studio) Inker: Horacio Ottolini Letterer: John Costanza Colorist: Prismacolor

GRRRROWL!

EEK!!

ONE GIANT STEP FOR MARVIN

Marvin the Martian likes to spend his time travelling the outer reaches of Space in his speed-of-light spaceship. Here we see him in a distant galaxy, discovering a previously unknown planet. Marvin decides to give his new planet a special name. To find out what it is ,fit all the words into the grid using the letters already in place to guide you. Then the middle section, reading across, will spell the new name.

| CONTACT | SOLID | PEST | BAND |
| COLOUR | NANNY | ROOM | SOYA |

77

WB1603

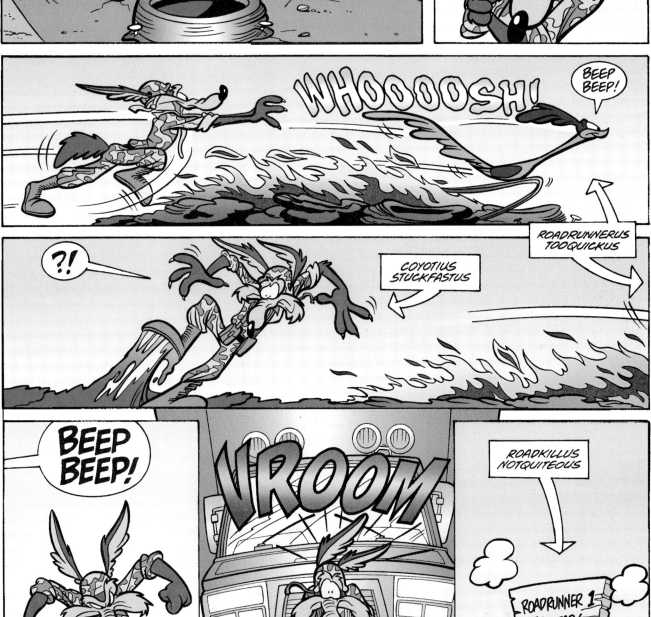

BUG'S AND LOLA'S SPACE JAM QUIZ

Bugs and Lola are having great fun, jamming on their hi-tech, state-of-the-art space instruments. They are playing tunes of their all-time, favourite pop group.
What is the group called?

Find out by answering these simple quiz questions about Earth music. Then transfer the numbered letters to the box at the bottom to spell the group's name.

Name of an instrument that you blow and the noise made by elephants.

T R U M P E T
1   2   3

Proper name for when someone sings on their own.

S O L O
4

Musical instrument played by angels!

H A R P
5   6

Noisy, circular, metal instruments that you clash together.

C Y M B A L S
7   8   9

Bugs is playing one of these in the picture.

G U I T A R
10   11

You play this flute-like instrument at First School and it has a very high-pitched sound.

R E C O R D E R
  12   13

Bugs' and Lola's fave, out-of-this -world group are-

T	H	E		S	P	A	C	E		G	I	R	L	S
1	5	3		4	2	6	7	12		10	11	13	8	9

Writer: Michael Eury Penciller: Omar Aranda (Sol Studio) Inker: Scott McRae Letterer: John Costanza Colorist: Prismacolor

I'M COMIN' IN, ONE WAY OR ANOTHER!

DETERMINED FELLER, AIN'T HE?

OOF!

I DIDN'T KNOW MY TV WAS 3-D!

EHHH... WHAT'S UP, DOC?

D-UHH... MY NAME AIN'T "DOC." IT'S MUGSY!

YEAH, YEAH, THAT'S NICE. SO TELL ME, WHY'D YOU DROP IN, UNINVITED-LIKE?

D-UHHH, ROCKY, MY BOSS... HE T'REW ME OUT! AN' AFTER ALL DA GOOD TIMES WE HAD-- BETTIN' ON HORSES, BREAKIN' KNEECAPS, ROBBIN' BANKS...

: SIGH : DOSE WERE DA DAYS.

87

89

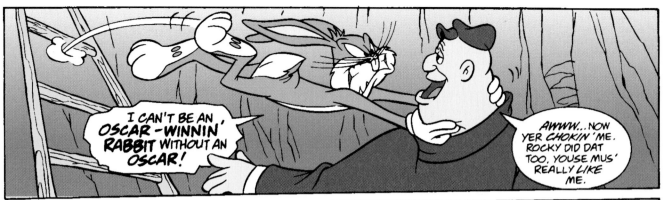

91

BUMPER SPACE FAIR WORDSEARCH

Taz, Daffy and Lola are enjoying an exciting ride on the bumper cars at the Space Funfair. But it is not their very favourite sideshow.

Find the following words in the grid and cross them out. (They are spelt in all directions, including backwards). Then transfer the left-over letters to the bottom of the page and it will spell the three chums' top attraction at the fair.

R	I	F	L	E	R	A	N	G	E
G	O	L	D	F	I	S	H	T	H
Y	E	U	S	T	E	E	W	S	S
B	A	I	N	S	P	G	T	K	H
B	Y	L	R	D	O	R	C	U	O
H	O	O	P	L	A	U	I	N	T
C	H	Y	T	D	D	B	C	Z	A
S	T	S	M	E	G	D	O	D	E
L	L	L	A	B	H	C	N	U	P
B	I	G	W	H	E	E	L	E	T

GOLDFISH	HORSES
SHOT	HOOPLA
DODGEMS	PLAY
TOY	RIFLE RANGE
ROUNDABOUT	DARTS
BIG WHEEL	SWEETS
DUCKS	PUNCHBALL
PRIZE	

T H E _ _ B I G

B O U N C Y

C A S T L E

93

Writer: David Cody Weiss   Penciller: David Alvarez   Inker: Mike DeCarlo   Letterer: John Costanza   Colors: Prismacolor

I AM GWAD TO SEE YOU GETTING EXERCISE, PUDDY!

NATCH! I'VE ALWAYS BEEN PHYSICALLY FIT! THERE'S ONLY ONE PROBLEM--

EXERCISIN' WORKS UP A CAT'S APPETITE!

I'M GOING DOWN TO THE MAILBOX, BOYS --BE GOOD WHILE I'M GONE!

YOU GONNA WEAD ME A STORY, PUDDY?

MAYBE LATER-- AFTER DINNER. 'SIDES, THESE BOOK AIN'T FOR READIN'!

OOH, GOODY! A WAMP! YOU GONNA DO SOME TWICKS?

UH-HUH! I'M GONNA TRY OUT MY DISAPPEARIN ACT -- YOU CAN BE MY PARTNER!

TWEETY! TWEETY! YOU GOT A LETTER!

THE RETURN ADDRESS SAYS IT CAME ALL THE WAY FROM WASHINGTON!

OH, THIS IS SO EXCITING! "DEAR TWEETY: THE TIME HAS COME FOR ME TO VISIT WITH MY FAVORITE NEPHEW."

"AS YOU KNOW, YOUR UNCLE SAMMY LIKES TO FLY AS CHEAPLY AS POSSIBLE...."

PHOOEY! I NEVER GET ANY MAIL!

"TO AVOID HIGH AIRLINE FARES AND THE STRESS OF A CROSS-COUNTRY FLIGHT, I HAVE DISCOVERED A NEW WAY TO TRAVEL."

HEH. THE OLD GUY MUST BE GETTING PRETTY LONG IN THE TOOTH.

MIGHT BE A BIT CHEWY, BUT I LIKE MY FOOD SEASONED!

"I WILL BE ARRIVING ON THE TENTH VIA OVERNIGHT MAIL. I FIND THIS TO BE THE CHEAPEST AND MOST RELIABLE METHOD FOR A BIRD ON A BUDGET.

"I NOW USE THEM FOR ALL MY JOURNEYS! AFTER ALL-- I GET TO BRING MY BEDROOM WITH ME ... AND BAD WEATHER DOESN'T EVEN SLOW THE POST OFFICE DOWN!"

MY, ISN'T THAT INTERESTING -- A BIRD WHO TRAVELS BY POSTAL PACKAGE! YOU HAVE THE MOST CHARMING RELATIVES, TWEETY.

THE TENTH, EH? FIVE DAYS FROM NOW ... MORE THAN ENOUGH TIME TO GET READY TO SAY "BON APPÉTIT" TO OUR GUEST!